HODJA

ISBN, 975 - 439 - 002 - 9

HODJA

KARTPOSTAL ve YAYINLARI
MATBAACILIK SANAYİ ve TİCARET A.Ş

Ankara Caddesi 60/1 Sirkeci — İSTANBUL
Tel: 522 45 08 — 519 15 21 — 519 41 23

Compiled by
M. Ali BİRANT

Translated by
Ece BİRANT

Illustration by
Göker Grafik Ajansı
Yurdagün GÖKER
Tel: 528 17 74

Typo by
AND Tel: 522 84 07

Arrangement
AND

Photos by
Arshiver of AND

Nasreddin Hodja picture, no 2142, in the Royal Treasury Office at Topkapı Palace Museum

NASREDDİN HODJA

The years in which Nasreddin Hodja lived, have. never been clearly established.
He was a master of humour, with a fund of wisdom. In his anecdotes, Turks look at
life with an attitude of mind which points out the humour of a situation while
causing us to think. Hodja is represented as a Turkish master of humour.

It is said that (Nasreddin) Hodja was born in Hortu (Nasreddin Hodja's village in
Sivrihisar near Eskişehir in 1208.) His father was the village imam, named Abdullah
Efendi and his mother was a housewife named Sıdıka Hatun. He completed his early
education in his village, then he finished his education by attending medresses in
Sivrihisar and Konya. It is known that he was taught by Seyid Mahmud Hayrani in
Sivrihisar and he was taught by Seyid Haci İbrahim Sultan in Konya.

Hodja made friends with the famous scientists in his day. One of the pieces of
information about Hodja is that after his father's death, he went to Akşehir following his teacher Hodja Seyid Mahmut Hayrani who had settled down in Akşehir
before Hodja's father's death.

Hodja who was educated very well, had become an assistant of a Kadi in Akşehir
and in Konya, apart from this he had become a teacher in medresses. It is certainly
known that Hodja taught one of the most important books of Hanefian canonical
Kudur-i Şerif.

Hodja, whose name in known almost everywhere in the world, who's anecdotes
have become a subjest of common talk and who's life and character have become a
myth, was a man of genius. His every word caused his listeners to lough. Hodja so
perspicacious that he brought his listeners face to face with the truth as he caused
them to burst out laughing. The listeners understood the truth in a subtle way at
the same time as they laughed.

Hodja's style is very different from the other humourist. His style, makes his anecdotes very famous and enjoyable.

In Hodja's anecdotes it is easy to see weaknesses of human character. It is as if he
enables us to see people's characters with his genius. To learn a lesson from the
mirror held up before us, is our task. Every person should be able to go deeper and
deeper into the human soul according to his or her ability.

Hodja's words will be as popular in the future as they were in his own time.

But it is known that some anecdotes which are still told don't belong to Hodja.

They have been told up to now as a memorial to Hodja's character. Without doubt,
the first storytellers of these types of anecdotes were people who understood Hodja's philosophy very well.

Nasreddin Hodja tomb in Akşehir
"Tomb's surroundings are clear and a large padlock is hanged on its door."

The anecdotes that are thought to belong to Hodja reflect his philosophy on life, and have been accepted by people as proverbs and sayings all over the world, being told from one country to another. Being the works of Turks' hing imagination, these anecdotes are worth appreciation and will continue living in countless languges and countries by being told from one generation to another.

Nasreddin Hodja lived in a beautiful house in Akşehir and he died in the same house. His tomb was first built by Seljuks. It isn't established when the tomb was built, but it is known that his tomb began to break down in the Ottoman period and was rebuilt in the period of Sultan Abdülhamid II in 1905.

The Akşehir council rebuilt Hodja's tomb and other graves near the tomb by' using the original shape of the tomb as an example.

Also at Hodja's tomb we can see his philosophy of humour. Three sides of the tomb are open, on one of the open side doors there is a big lock and this is an important factor in explaining Hodja's philosophy.

As a second example the date of Hodja's death was written in reverse to draw attention to how Hodja used to ride on his donkey. Visitors to Hodja's tomb read the date 386, as the date of Hodja's death . The true date of his death is in 683 on the Moslem calendar (Christian calendar 1284)

Every year, between July 5th and July 10th, a Hodja Festival takes place in Akşehir. During this festival, Hodja's life and philosophy are brought to people's attention.

These words about Hodja are very few. The investigator who works on Hodja's life will write a lot of books with many pages.

As we finish, we have chosen some of Hodja's anecdotes and illustrated them, hoping you will enjoy them. From the following anecdote we understand that Hodja had taught in a medresse.

TO PUT YOUR BABY TO SLEEP

Hodja was seen at the gate of the medresse with his students around him and the important canonical book of Hanefian under his arm. A woman with her crying child in her arms came towards the gate.

"Hodja, please recite to my child, it never sleeps during the day and during the night". She said.

Hodja's eyes suddenly began to glitter. He thought it, was time to give his students a good lesson. After mesmerizing his students with his eyes, Hodja gave the woman the book under his arm and said:

"Dear lady, take this book and read it when you want to make your baby sleep."
"Hodja, will this book relly put my baby to sleep?" the woman asked amazed.
Hodja thought it was the right time to make a clever retort:
"Dear lady, it has been proved with my experience a few minutes ago. I' ve just finished the lesson, and these students were sleeping soundly when I was reading that book."

Nasreddin Hodja monument in Sivrihisar.

The expression of "Centre of the world" is written under it.

I WENT TO NASRETTIN HODJA'S VILLAGE HORTU

I went to Nasrettin Hodja's village of Hortu, where Nasrettin Hodja was born and brought up. The village where Hodja was born is after Sivrihisar, 4 km. off to the right - Hand side of the highway between Eskişehir and Ankara - There is the "Nasrettin Hodja Restaurant and Service Station" on the highway, almost 150 m before the road enters the village. Should tourists intending to visit the village, stop at this service station, they may receive the first information about Hodja and his village.

It was a thundering day when I stopped at this service station and went into the restourant to take a rest and get some information, about Hodja's village. I asked the waiter who broughtme my tea, for some information, Saying, "Just a moment, sir" he went away, but he was soon in frent of me with his friend named Necmi. He said, "Sir, my friend Necmi will give you all the information about Hodja's village".

Then, I asked Necmi for some information about the village. He asked me whether I had a car or not, and I said I did.

"I was going to the village myself, and it will be my pleasure to guide you to the village "he said. So we got into the car and set off.

My guide Necmi, who was a vigorous, swarthy village fellow, began to give me much very useful information about Hodja and the history of his village, along the way. I noticed that my companion was speaking easily and finishing his sentence with humorous worlds. A   result I could not help saying; "You remind me of Nasrettin Hodja with your humorous expressions."

He smiled saying, "As a matter of fact, they call me Hodja's grandson in the village."

After a short pouse we were in the village, Pointing to the marble stone looking like an historical work leaning against the wall of the village elementary school, my

Hortu village, birth place of Nasreddin Hodja

Outer door of the house of ˙Nasreddin Hodja

guide Necmi explained, "This marble stone used to belong to the bathhouse which was run by Hodja's father".

A little turther on, he showed me a patterned marble stone fitted into the base of the minaret belonging to the village mosque, and wenton, "This stone is also remnant from the historical bathhouse. It was fitted into the base of the minaret in order to be kept safe."

I asked my quide, "Well then where is this historical bathhouse?"
"It is further ahead, " he replied.
We began walking. On our way, he showed me a marble stone in the shape of a wash basin, called basin stone, and said.
"This stone has also remained from the some bathhouse"

We were walking... as if the village houses and the twisting roads were leading us back into a remote history. We felt as if we were living in Hodja's century. We stopped in front of a house. "This is the house where Nasrettin Hodja was born and brought up" said my guide. Full of indescribable feelings, we visited the house, wandered and sat in it and let ourselves go into the world of imagination...

Later on, we went to the region called the reed bed of the village. This place was a rough steep area. There was a stream running down wards. We climbed down to the banks of the stream. My guide pointed to a ruin and said, "Here are the foundation stones of the bathhouse run by Hodja's father."
He showed me the water flowing a fev steps ahead. That is said to be the healing spring water they used to use in the bathhouse. This healing water is said to be especially good for jaundice. Moreover, Hodja's father, is said to have known this characteristic of the water so well that, he used to keep his patients in the relaxing room and make them take baths with this water for twenty days, and the patients are said to have returned to their villages in good health. Hodja's father, who is said to have healed many patients, has been remembered as a kind philanthropist, in the district. And Hodja is said to have helped his father as long as he lived in the village during his childhood and youth. He was obuiously influenced a great deal by his father " said my guide, and stopper talking as if he wanted to leave me alone with my thoughts.

The conclusion is that, Nasrettin Hodja, who is character known world-wide with his intelligence, humorous speech and care in helping people, was born and spent his childhood in this village as the son of this philanthropist family.

Those marvellous stories and anecdotes of Hodja will be told and retold all over the world for ever, making people laugh and think at the same time.

The statue of Nasreddin Hodja and childs

The house of Nasreddin Hodja.

Furnace of the house of
Nasreddin Hodja

This the ruin of Nasreddin Hodja's
father's baht.

This the stone basin of Nasreddin Hodja's
father's baht.

HIS SLEEP HAS ESCAPED

Hodja was wandering about in the street late at night. Some night-watchmen approached and asked him, "what are you doing out here at this time of the night, man?" Hodja replied mockingly, "Well, my sleep has escaped an and I'm trying to catch it !"

WOULD IT HAVE REMAINED UNTIL NOW?

One of his neighbours asked Hodja, "Have you got some fourty year old vinegor, my friend?" Hodja nodded, "Yes, I have". Then the man requested, "Could, you give me a cup of it?" "No I can't", Hodja replied, "Would it have lasted until now if I had given a cup of it to everybody asking for it?"

AND SHE THINKS

Hodja Nasreddin was wandering around in the market place one morning and he saw that a man with a cage in his hand was shouting. He was selling his parrot for 100 gold ducas. Hodja bewildered by this comotion, ran to his house. He beleived that he had found how to make a profit and grabbing the turkey that he fed in his garden, Hodja went back to the bazaar. So he began:

— 200 gold ducas! This turkey is for sale for 200 ducas! But nobody seemed to be interested in this shooping. One or two men came closer and took a look at the turkey and continued uninterested.

Hodja waited there for a long time; at last one of his friends came near and asked:

— Hodja, are you mad? how can you sell an ordinary turkey for such a high price?

Unaware of the specialities of a parrot, Hodja answered:

—Oh, come on my friend. That man sold his cute bird for 100 ducas. Why can not I sell my gorgeous turkey for 200?

BAD – TEMPERED DONKEY

Hodja had taken his donkey to the market to sell it.

Some people came near to have a look at the donkey.

One of the men wanted to raise its tail, the donkey lashed the man with both feet. Another one wanted to examine its teeth with his hands and if bit the man's hand.

For this reason no one could approach the donkey, from fear.

"Hodja, this donkey is very bad - tempered. It isn't worth a cent," Said one of the buyers.

Hodja realised that the donkey wouldn't be sold and began to act like a thick--skinned person.

"I also know that it isn't worth a cent. I look it to the market so that everyone will understand what trouble I have with it, " he answered.

WHY DON'T YOU EAT AN OMELETTE?

Hodja liked omelettes and wanted to eat one with cheese and honey. He straight away into a shop.

"Do you have eggs?" he asked the shopkeeper.

"Yes, I have eggs daily" the shopkeeper answered.

"Well, do you have honey and butter too?" he asked again.

When the shopkeeper said. "Yes I have.", Hodja lost his temper and began to shout at him.

"Why don't you cook and eat an omelette then?"

THE WRONG WAY

One day Naṣreddin Hodja got on his donkey the wrong way, facing towards the back

—Hodja, the people said, you are sitting on your donkey backwards!

—No, he replied. It's not that I am sitting on my donkey backwards, the donkey is facing the wrong way!

MISSING INGREDIENT

Hodja and his friends were chatting together one day and the subject of the chat turned out to be food. Now this was what Hodja liked very much to talk about and he happily listened to the men discribing their favourite foods. One of his friends asked Hodja:

—Hodja, which food do you like best?

Hodja without hesitation, answered:

I like helva best, (Helva is a kind of dessert made of flour, butter, sugar, etc.) and he continued, but, unfortunately, there is no opportunity for me to eat it nowadays.

His friends asked why this was so and Hodja answered:

— Well, when there was flour there was no sugar at home. I had some sugar but then there was no butter. When I had butter I could not find any flour, so I could not have that delicious helva.

— Allright, said his friends, but surely there was a moment when all that stuff was at home.

Hodja answered sorrowfully:

— Well, then I wasn't at home.

A MISER

A miser to Hodja; "You mean to say you also like money, Hodja, but can you tell me why you like money so much, please?"

"Because it doesn't let me be in need of people like you" he replies.

A PORTER FOR TEN DAYS

Hodja asked a porter to carry his things. While they were walking in the street he lost the porter. He searched thoroughly but in vain, he couldn't find him. He gave up hope of both the things and the porter.

After ten days he saw the lost porter and changed his direction to avoid being seen by the porter.

The men with him asked why he acted like that. He explained;

"The porter has been carrying my things for ten days. If he wanted ten days' pay, what would I do?"

WHO IS THE REAL THIEF?

One day a thief entered Hodja's house. Hodja woke up and got up very quietly. Without being detected, he hid the thief's shoes.

The thief searched the house but he couldn't find anything worth stealing, and he came back to the door to leave, but he couldn't find his shoes. Helpless, the thief rushed out of the house barefoot.

At that time Hodja began to shout;

"Catch him, he is a thief"

The neighbours caught the thief who was barefoot. The thief bitterly looked at the people who caught him and said;

"Have a sense of justice", pointing to Hodja "I broke into his house, that's my fault, but he stole my shoes".

THE VALUABLE ASS

Once upon a time Hodja was badly in lack of money. He did not know how to manage this problem. Finally he decided to go to the market and sell his ass.

But it was not as he expected and nobody seemed to be interested. At last a man came near Hodja to ask about the ass. The man decided to play a trick and said :

— This animal is no good. First of all it is too old. It can not even carry a small weight, it is ill. Soon it will die. But since you have come all the way here I would like to do a good deed. I will give you 10 akçes. (Akçe is a unit of money used in the early Ottoman Period.)

Hodja was quite surprised, as he had hoped for a better price for his ass. But there was nothing that he could do, so he bargained and sold the ass for 15 akçes.

As soon as he bought the ass the man began to shout :

— Listen everybody, here is an excellent ass! It is young and strong. Better then the finest horse. It can carry any kind of weight.

The people in the market began to gather around the man and the price of the ass quickly increased.

— I'll pay 25 akçes,

— I'll pay 30!..

— No, I'll buy it for 40 akçes...

— 45 akçes...

Hodja saw that his animal suddenly became very valuable. He could not bare it any more. So he said :

— Stop it, I'll buy the ass for 50 akçes.

He paid the money and brought the ass back home. Hodja's wife was surprised :

— Did not you sell the ass? she said.

— What are you talking about? Hodja said. I did not know how valuable our ass was. If I had not bought it back for 50 akçes, we would really have lost.

CHILD DISCIPLINE

One day Nasreddin Hodja told his son to go and get some water from the well. He told him not to break the pitcher and then he proceeded to give him a hard spanking.

—Hodja, asked a spectator, why do you spank your son when he hasn't done anything wrong?

—Because it would be too late to punish him after he broke the pot, wouldn't it?

MALE OR FEMALE

A man asked Hodja, "Was the pigeon that brought the olive branch in its beak to Noha's Ark, male or female?"

"Of course it was male, if it was female it wouldn't have been able to keep its beak shut for such a long time." was the answer of Hodja.

A **Hittite banquet** appears in relief on this stone slab, which was carved during the 800's B.C.

A QUESTION AND AN ANSWER

Hodja's wise replies for even very complicated questions was known by everyone and frequently people tried to upset him by asking very hard ones.

One day a friend asked Hodja this question:

— Hodja, why do all these people go in different directions when they start off for Business in the morning, instead of going in the same direction?

— Well, my friend, said Hodja quickly, if they went all in the same direction the balance of the world would suddenly be upset.

BEFORE IT IS TOO LATE

A chattering woman, one of Hodja's neighbours, came to Hodja and said:

— Oh Hodja, can you say something and give advice to my daughter. I can not keep her quiet and calm. She ruins everything.

Hodja answered the woman:

— My dear neighbour, what your girl needs is not advice but a young husband. Then you will see how she changes and becomes silent as you wish. You look for such a boy, before it is too late.

I CAN GIVE YOU ONLY THE FIXED DATE

A friend of Hodja asked him for some money and a fixed date to pay it back.

"I can't give you the money because I don't have it, but I can give you the fixed date." Hodja said.

THE RIGHT ANSWER

Hodja Nasreddin, returning from a visit to the town, was accompaigned by a friend well-known for his stinginess. At noon they decided to relax in a shadow and eat. They were going to share a pot of yoghurt that they bought in town.

They sat under a big tree and took their spoons out of their sacks. His friend took out a sack of sugar and began to pour it on his half of yoghurt and began to eat saying:

—.I like to eat the yoghurt with sugar on it.

Hodja was quite mad at the man's stinginess and decided to play a joke so he took a bottle of vinegar out of his sack,

Noticing Hodja's intention his friend interrupted:

— Hodja, what are you going to do with that bottle of vinegar?

Hodja answered:

— Oh, I like to eat yoghurt with vinegar so I'll pour it on my share.

The man objected:

— But Hodja, if the vinegar floods over to my share, you will spoil the yoghurt all.

Hodja smiled wisely and looked at him :

— Then, my dear friend, pour the sugar on my share too, if you don't mind.

IN THE DARK

Hodja Nasreddin and his wife woke up when it was past midnight. It was very dark in the room. Hodja's wife told him to light the candle.

— Where is the candle? Hodja asked sleeply.

—It is on your right side.

Hodja answered back with drowsiness:

— Come on my dear, how shall I know my right or left side in this dark.

TO BE BORN AND TO DIE

A talkative man asked Hodja "Hodja, untill when will people Continue to be born and to die in this way?"

"Until Heaven and Hell are full of crops" Hodja answered this unreasnable man.

WHAT IS MARRIAGE?

Hodja was asked "What is marriage, Hodja?"
"During the day to quarrel together and during the night to snore together" he answered.

IF I WAS ON IT

One day Hodja lost his donkey. While looking for it he was also rejoicing. When the people saw him they couldn't figure out why he was so happy, and they wanted to find out the reason for this so Hodja told them:
—I'm happy because I wasn't riding the donkey when it got lost. If I had been I'd be lost now too!

HE WHO WAS ANGRY

Somebody asked Hodja a rediculous question:
— Hodja are you at odds with those who married before you or after you got married?
— Both answered Hodja
— Why is that ? asked the man again
— Why not? I am angry with the ones who got married before me because they did not give me any advice. The ones who got married after me are angry with me because they did not get any advice from me.

THEY'RE PLAYING MUSIC

Hodja was returning home one night with one of his students when he was a gang of thieves standing in front of a house, trying to break the lock. Hodja parcaived that he would probably get hurt if he spoke up, so he decided to stay quiet and pass by quickly. But his student, however, did not understand what was happening So he asked:

—What are all those men standing there doing?

—Shhh! replied Hodja. They're playing music!

—But I can't hear anything!

—Well, we shall hear the music tomorrow! Hodja said.

NOT TO CAUSE TROUBLE

When Hodja was cutting wood in the forest, a wolf ate his donkey. As Hodja was looking at the running wolf a man shouted to Hodja,

"Run Hodja, the wolf is escaping."

"Don't shout in vain, somehow or other I lost my donkey, at least let the wolf run uphill without having any trouble in addition to his excessively filled stomach".

THE WAY TO BE A GOOD MAN

During a talk a person asked Hodja;

"Hodja, how can I be a good man?"

Hodja shook his head from one side to the other and replied.

"You should listen to a person if he speaks and you should speak if a person listens to you."

ASK THE MULE

His friends mounted Hodja Nasreddin on a mule, but a very obstinate one, to play a game with him.

As soon as Hodja Nasreddin got on the animal it began to shake him wildly. Realizing that he might fall down immediately Hodja Nasreddin held on to the saddle tight and the mule ran as fast as it could.

His friends shouted after him:

— Where are you going Hodja ?

Hodja struggling with animal and trying to stay on the saddle answered back:

— Don't ask me ask the mule.

I AM CARRYING THE SACK

Hodja Nasreddin went to the market one day and bought a lot of goods. Later he found the sack in which he put the food very heavy, so he sat on the back of the ass and put the sack on his shoulder.

His friends who saw him in this position asked:

— Why don't you put that heavy sack on the back of the ass instead of you carrying it?

— Can't you see, the poor animal can not even carry me. How can I load him with this heavy sack, too?

SHALL I GO FURTHER?

One night Hodja and his wife were sleeping in their bed. She told him to get a little further away. Hodja got up immediately, put on his clothes, went out, and set out on his way.

After he walked a long way, he met one of his friends in the morning. The man asked Hodja where he was going so early.

Hodja said,

"I don't know. Please go and ask my wife if she wants me to go further. I'll wait here, till you bring me the answer."

HODJA'S WILL

Hodja lay in bed with a serious illness, but he kept on making jokes. He said one day to his friends that came to visit him :

— If I die, never bury me in a new grave. Note that it should be an old one.

His friends asked curiously:

— Hodja, why do you wish so?

— Well, my friends, when the angels come after I die, I'll tell them that I have been already questioned and show them the old grave as the proof. So maybe I can be passed by.

I NOW ACCEPT NINETY NINE COINS

Hodja was offered ninety nine silver coins in his dream.

"I won't accept them unless you give me a hundred coins" he said.

Just at that moment he woke up and saw that there was nothing in his hands, his hands were empty. He immediately shut his eyes and opened his hands and said:

"I now accept the coins you've offered me even if they are only ninety nine."

ARCHERY

Once King Timur took Hodja into the fields where his archers were practicing. Hodja boasted:

—I am excellent at archery!

The King didn't believe him so he forced Hodja to take his bow and shoot some arrows at the target. The first one he shot missed the target entirely. Hodja laughed:

—Ha! That's how the magistrate shoots!

The second shot also missed the target complately. Again he laughed:

—Ha! That's how the mayor shoots!

His third shot, by a fluke hit the tarket squarely in the bullseye. He chuckled.

—Aha! And that's how Nasreddin Hodja shoots!

A LADDER TO THE SKY

One day some priests wanted to annoy Hodja and asked him this question:
"How did your prophet Mohammad ascend to Heaven? Can you tell us, Hodja?"
Hodja replied to them in this way;
"It is very easy to answer that question. My Prophet ascended to Heaven with the ladder that your Prophet Jesus left behind."

WOULDN'T I GET OFF ANYWAY?

One day while Hodja was travelling on his donkey, the donkey shied and dropped Hodja off. A pack of children, men and women came together around Hodja and began to laught mockingly.

"Why are you laughing, wouldn't I get off anyway?" said Hodja as if he didn't fall down.

SHE KNOWS SWIMMING

In those times a healthy man could marry more than one women. Hodja also married a young woman a few years after his first marriage. But it was quite difficult to manage two women in the same house since they used to quarrel always. Every time Hodja came home he saw that the women were fighting with each other.

One night he came home and saw that the women were fighting again. He tried to stop them. The older wife told Hodja that they were quarreling about him and asked him which one he loved more. Hodja hoping to settle the matter said that he loved both of them.

The older one, not satisfied with this answer, said:

— No, you should love one of us more than the other.

The younger one included:

— Suppose that the three of us went out to the sea in o boat and the boat sank. Which one of us would you save first?

Hodja Nasreddin, confused with this compticated question, stopped and thought. Then looking towards his older wife he said:

My dear, I think you know a little swimming, don't you?

THE WILL

Hodja Nasreddin became ill and had to stay in bed for a long time. During my this time many of his friends and neighbors visited him to wish him good health. But each one used to stay for a couple of hours and poor Hodja was very tired out.

One day, again, some of his friends visited him and stayed for a long time and Hodja was as bored as he could be. When the men were leaving one of them said:

— Hodja, I hope you will be alright very soon, but you know man is mortal and something might happen and you may die. Have you thought about your will?

Hodja answered back:

— My will is this, all should learn never to sit so long when visiting an ill person.

THE GOLD COIN

Hodja was sitting in a tea shop when a stranger came in and asked him :
— Hodja, can you change this gold coin for me? I need the money.

Hodja didn't have any money to change it with but he didn't want to admit this in front of his friends. So he took the gold piece and held it thoughtfully in his hand and said:

—This coin is underweight. I cannot change it for you at its face value.

—Then just give me what you think it's worth, replied the man.

But it's very, very much underweight, insisted Hodja.

—Oh no, what a shame! replied the man. But I need the change and I'd really appreciate it if you could give me whatever little you think it's worth .

—Hodja, seeing that this man was not going to give up and not wanting to lose face before his friends, said to him:

—This coin is so much underweight that if I change it, you will owe me money!

MORE LIGHT HERE

One day Hodja lost his gold ring inside the house somewhere. After looking for a while not finding it, he went outside to look for it there. His neighbour asked him what he was looking for.

—I'm looking for my ring, Hodja replied.
—Where did you lose it? asked the neighbour.
—Somewhere in the house, said Hodja.
—Then why are looking for it outside?
—Because there's more light out here, he answered.

I NEITHER BOUGHT NOR SOLD A MOON

While Hodja was wandering in the market, a man came near and greeted him.
"Hodja, what date is it today according to the moon?" he asked. Since Hodja understood the man's purpose, he answered his question in this way:
"I don't know. I neither bought nor sold a moon up to now".

THE PROOF

One day a priest arrived at Akşehir. He said that he had some **questions to ask** and nobody could answer them up to this time and that he wanted **to question** the cleverest man of the village. The villagers quickly brought him to Hodja Nasreddin.

The priest sat near him and said:

— I have got two questions to ask you. Nobody has been able to **answer** them yet. I want to see if you can. Here is the first one: can you tell me how many stars there are in the sky?

Hodja answered without hesitation:

— If you can count the hairs on my donkey you will find the number.

— Come on now. How can you count the hair of a donkey?

— Allright then, answered Nasreddin, how can you count all the stars in the sky?

The priest seemed to accept this answer and asked the second question.

— Then tell me, how many hairs do I have in my beard?

— As many as the hairs in my donkey's tail, answered Hodja.

— How can you prove it?

— It is quite easy said Hodja. I will pull a hair from your beard for each one from the donkey's tail. If there are any left on my donkey's tail or on your chin, than I was wrong.

43

A WONDERFUL THOUGHT

One day Hodja asked his wife to make some helva, a very delicious sweet made from sesame seeds, honey, and other ingredients. She made quite a lot and Hodja ate nearly all of it.

That night in bed he woke her up and said:

—I've just had a wonderful thought!

—Bring me the rest of the helva and I'll tell you. .

She got up and brought him the helva and when he had finished eating it she said:

—Now I won't be able to go back to sleep until you tell me your thought.

—The Thought, said Hodja, was this: Never go to sleep without finishing all the helva that has been made that day!

I'VE GOT THE RECIPE

Hodja Nasreddin wanted to eat stew and bought a big peace of liver in the market. He did not know how to cook it, so he went to the cook and got the recipe. Now everything was going all right and he would eat a fine stew at home tonight.

While dreaming of the dinner and walking a kite plunged down to Hodja, grabbet the liver and flew away.

Hodja was desperate. There was nothing he could do except to say goodbye to the stew. But then, remembering, he put this hand in his pocket and took out a piece of paper shouting after the bird:

— Oh no, you stupid. You won't be able to eat my dinner because I've got the recipe!

IN ANY CASE

Once upon a time, Hodja had a well-fed lamb which he liked very much.

One day Hodja's friends said; "The last judgement day will come very soon and all of us will die. At least, let's kill your lamb and eat it."

Hodja never paid any attention, but they insisted on killing the lamb.

In the end Hodja didn't object any more and gave them permission to kill the lamb.

They met under some trees by a river. The lamb was cooked on a fire and then eaten. After they ate the lamb they took off their clothes; some of them began to wrestle and some of them went swimming. Hodja was alone by the fire. They told Hodja not to put out the fire.

Hodja gathered the clothes and threw them into the fire. A few minutes later his friends came back and they didn't find their clothes.

They realised that Hodja threw them into the fire, "What did you do Hodja?" they scolded him.

Hodja replied confidently;

"What will you use the clothes for? Look the fire is burning well. The last judgement day will come very soon anyway."

HOW MANY YARDS IN LENGTH IS THE WORLD?

One day Hodja was asked

"I wonder how many yards long in length is the world, Hodja?" At that time a funeral procession was passing. Hodja pointed to the procession and said.

"You should ask your question to the one inside that coffin, because he has measured and computed the width and length of the world and he is going away."

PLEASURE OF RETRIEVING

One day Hodja lost his donkey and he immediately ran to the market place and began to cry.

"To the one who finds and brings me my donkey, I'll give it to him with its pack saddle."

Hodja's friends and acquaintances didn't believe what they heard, they approached Hodja.

"Hodja, as you'll give the finder your donkey, why are you crying so?" they asked.

Hodja answered this question by shaking his head; "Just to experience the pleasure of retrieving something I've lost."

HOW CAN A MAN BITE HIS OWN EAR?

A plaintiff and a defendant came to the court while Hodja was judge. The plaintiff pointed to the defendant and said,

"This man bit my ear."

The defendant was asked if he did this, but he tried to defend himself.

"I'm not guilty, he bit his ear himself".

Hodja thought a lot about it but he couldn't come to a conclusion, so he postponed the lawsuit till the afternoon.

During the rest, Hodja began to wonder if a man could bite his own ear and decided to have try, but he fell down from the sofa and banged his head, and his head began to bleed.

When the lawsuit began in the afternoon, the plaintiff asked,

"How can it be possible? How can one bite his own ear?"

Hodja explained his judgement pointing to his head.

"Even if a man can't bite his own ear, he bangs his head and may injure his ear as he is trying to bite it".

FORTUNATELY

While Hodja was ploughing his field, a big thorn went into his foot. I was such a thorn that it pierced into his rawhide sandal and got into his foot. Hodja pulled out the thorn with difficulty. And then he said;

"Thank God, I didn't put on my new rawhide sandals which I bought last year."

AT THE POLICE STATION

One day someone stole the Hodja's donkey so he immediately went to the Police Station and reported the theft. The Chief of Police said:

—Now Hodja, this is serious. We'll do all we can to get your donkey back. After all, are rather famous. Now please, start at the beginning and tell me exactly how it happened.

Hodja replied:

—Well, since I wasn't there when it happened, how am I supposed to know?

THE HAIR AND THE BEARD

The hair of a man is usually unstable but his beard always is the same. Hodja's hair turned out to be all white when he became older, but not even a single hair of his beard was pale.

While he was having a haircut by the barber one day, one of his friends asked him:

— Hodja, your hair is almost white, but why is your beard as black as coal?

Hodja answered him wisely:

— That's quite easy my friend, because my hair is 20 years older than my beard.

THE DEATH OF HIS DONKEY

One day Hodja was heart-broken over the loss of his dear wife. All of his neighbors and friends tried to encourage and comfort him by saying:

—Don't worry about her, Hodja, we'll help you to find an even better wife!

A short while later his donkey died also but Hodja seemed to mourn even more over the loss of his donkey than over the loss of his wife. Some of his friends noticed this and so they approached him concerning this matter, and he replied:

—When my wife passed away all my friends promised me that they would find an even better one for me, but so far no one has offered to replace my donkey!

IT'S STRUCK TWO

Hodja Nasreddin used to deal with several businesses during his life but none of them lasted for more than a few weeks.

The latest business that Hodja dealed in was to open a shop where he sold clocks. But soon after the little boys of the neighbourhood began to bother him by asking frequently what the time was.

Hodja tried to be patient for a couple of days but this was irresistible. So he obtained a stick and went to his shop one morning. Just a few minutis later the boys consulted him again and one of them asked:

— What time is it Hodja!

Hodja grabbed the stick at his moment and hit it on the boy's head twice, and included:

— Now, my boy, it's struck two.

WHO'S GOING TO SELL THE PICKLES

One day Hodja Nasreddin decided to sell pickles and make a profit out of this trade. He loaded his ass with the pickle pots and began to wander among the steets. He began to shout :

.– Pickles, I sell pickles...

But at his moment he was forced to become silent by the donkey's loud bray. Walking a few streets further Hodja tried to shout again. But the same moment he was stopped by tha loud bray again.. Poor Hodja had to keep quiet for the second time.

When Hodja Nasreddin tried for the third time, a few minuttes later, he again was interrupted with the bray of the ass. Losing his temper, Hodja cried at the ass nervously :

– That's enough of you, pal who is going to sell the pickles, "you " or I.

WHAT IS IT TO YOU?

One evening Hodja Nasreddin was walking back home when he met a friend on his way. The man said:

— Hodja. A few minutes ago I saw a man carrying a full tray of fine desserts.

— What is it to you? said the Hodja.

— But, said the man, he took the tray to your house.

Hodja looked at the man and said:

— Then what is it to you?

THEY HAVE STOPPED FIGHTING

At midnight Hodja heard a lot of commotion outside his window. He wrapped his blanket around himself and went outside to see what was happening. He saw two men fighting and he asked them why and tried to break it up. Without answering, one of them ripped the blanket off of the Hodja and both of them quickly ran away. So poor Hodja ashamedly walked back into his house naked and returned to his bed.

—What was all the fighting about? asked his wife

—It was over our blanket. Now that they have got our blanket they have stopped fighting!

WHICH INDISCREET

Hodja Nasreddin went to the market and bought peaches. Placing them in his pockets he kept to the way home. On his way he met children playing and called them near.

— Children, he said. If anyone knows what I have in my pocket, I'll give him the biggest peach.

The children all cried out:

— Peaches!

Hodja, surprised by the answer said:

— Which indiscreet fellow told you about this, and distributed all the peaches to the children.

HODJA'S SLIPPERS.

One day a group of young boys were playing under a large tree when they saw Hodja approaching so they said to each other:

—Let's trick Hodja! We'll get him to climb this tree and when he is up there, we'll take his slippers and run away!

—When Hodja came near them they danced and shouted!

—I can climb it! replied Hodja proudly.

Tucking his skirts into his belt, he took off his slippers and put them in the folds of his cloak.

—Hodja, why are you taking your slippers with you? asked the boys disappointedly.

—Ah, my boys, said Hodja, haven't you learned to guard your possessions carefully? Who knows what thief may come and steal them?

THE MOON IN THE WELL

One night Hodja was walking by a well when he had a sudden impulse to look inside of it. To his amazement he saw the reflection of the moon in the water and exclaimed:

—The moon has fallen into the well! I must save it somehow!

He looked around an found a rope with a hook on the end of it so he threw it in the well and shouted:

—Grab the hook, moon, and hold tight! I'll pull you out!

The rope latched onto a rock inside the well and Hodja pulled back on the rope as hard as he could. Suddenly the hook broke free from the rock and Hodja fell over on his back. Lying there, he noticed the moon high up in the sky above. He heaved a sigh of relief and said:

—Well, it wasn't easy, but it's sure a wonderful feeling to know that I've delivered the moon from the well!

THE FOUR OF US

Hodja Nasreddin's wife died ona day and his neighbours married him to a widow. But remembering her first husband she began every night just when they went to bed :

Oh my poor husband, what a good man he was...

She kept on doing this for a long period of time and, having not resisted Hodja Nasreddin began to praise his dead wife. But she did not seem either to understant or stop exclaiming.

One night, when they were in bed the woman began again and Hodja could not stant it. He pushed the woman and ròlled her down the bed.

— What have you done Hodja Efendi?

Hodja answered her angrily:

— That.s enough, it's you and me, my oldu wife and your old husband. Oh my god, how can the four of us sleep in one bed?

THERE ISN'T ANY DIFFERENCE

During a talk, Hodja said, "There isn't any difference between youth and old age".

The people at that place were confused with Hodja's comment and asked "Why not?"

Hodja had already prepared the answer.

"There is a stone in front of our house, I wasn't able to lift it in spite of trying many times when I was a young man."

"Recently, I remenbered and tried hard but I couldn't lift it again. For that reason, I understood that there isn't any difference between youth and old age."

WHO DO YOU BELIEVE?

One day a friend visited Hodja and said:

—Hodja, I want to borrow your donkey.

—I'm sorry, replied Hodja, but I've already lent it out to someone else.

As soon as he said this, the donkey brayed.

—But Hodja, I can hear the donkey! It's in the stable!

Shutting the door in this friend's face, Hodja told him with dignity:

—A man who believes the word of a donkey above my own, doesn't deserve to be lent anything!

I GOT RID OF THEM

Hodja's house suddenly caught fire one day and everybody in the neighbour-hood tried to save anything they could from the burning house. Hodja at this moment was smiling happily across from the house. One of this friends could not stand it and asked him:

— Hodja, your house is burning and you're standing here and smiling as if nothing was happening.

Hodja answered back:

— Sure I smile, my pal, at last I've got rid of those damn bed - bugs.

THE RIGHT OF NOTHING

Two men applied to Hodja Nasreddin when he was a judge in Akşehir. One of them was a poor porter. The other man accused the porter and said:

—This man was carrying a pile of wood on his back and he suddenly stumbled and dropped his load. I asked him what he would give me if I helped him to put the load on his back. He said that he vould give me "Nothing", now I want my right. I want him to give the "Nothing" which is my right.

Hodja listened to the man in silence and than said:

— Come closer my friend. Now raise the carpet on the floor and under it and tell me what you see there.

The man looked under the carpet and said:

— Nothing. There is nothing.

Hodja Nasreddin smiled and said:

— Good, now take that "Nothing" which is your right and get out of here.

A BARBER OR A BLACKSMITH

Hodja had gone to a barber's shop, but the barber was too inexperienced and his razor was too blunt. Hodja felt pain but the barber didn't care. Hodja began to sweat.

At that time a cry was heard from next door.

"What is happening there?" Hodja asked;

"Nothing, our neighbour is a blacksmith, I think they are nailing a mad ox, Hodja." the barber answered.

"To tell you the truth, I thought they were shaving one". Hodja said.

AT THE MILL

Once Hodja went into a nearby mill and began to take handfulls of grain out of the sacks and put them into his own. The miller came in and demanded:

—What are you doing here?

—I am a fool, quipped Hodja. I just have to do whatever comes into my mind!

—Well, how came it never came into your mind to take wheat out of your sack and put itt into mine?

—Sir, he replied, I am just a normal fool. I am not an absolute idiot!

UNLESS YOU ARE INSIDE

One day the neighbors were confused in a funeral procession. They were arguing about on which side of the coffin to walk and there were different opinions. Having not decided they went to Hodja Nasreddin for a conclusion. Hodja listened to each one silently and realized that no one would be satisfied with his suggestion, since each one believed his idea to be better than the other. So he smiled and, to everyone's surprise answered:

— It does not matter on which side of the coffin you are... unless it is the inside!

On ... own to rest under the
shade ... while and said:

— ... grow on such a tiny
stalk ...

J ... t on the head. Hodja
rubb ...

— ... head would have been

seri ...

THE WAY TO MARKET

One day Hodja was taking his chickens to market to sell. As he was approaching the market he opened the cages and took the chickens out and drove them in front of him. He wanted to take them in this way. The chickens began to run away to different places. Hodja lost his temper and getting a stick he walked towards the conceited cock amongst the chickens.

"You conceited cock, you know the coming of the morning and how to wake people from their sleep, but you don't know the way to market" he scolded.

YOU DIDN'T FALL

One day Hodja was working on the roof of his house. He must have felt dizzy because he found himself on the ground. Many people came near Hodja and asked these questions:

"How did you fall, Hodja?"

"Did you hurt yourself?"

"Why didn't you pay attention; Hodja?"

Hodja, who was tired of these questions answered.

"Whatever I say is in vain, if any of you had fallen from the roof, he would have known what I felt."

A THIEF

One night a thief broke into Hodja's house.

—Honey, wispered his wife, there's a thief in the next room!

—Shhh! Perhaps he will find something worth stealing, and then we can easily take it away from him!

SHE MIGHT HAVE LOST SOMETHİNG ELSE

One day a friend of Hodja said to him.

"Hodja, your wife is said to have lost her mind."

Hodja started to think deeply.

"Why are you thinking, Hodja?" the man asked.

"My wife has never had a mind, and now I wonder if she has lost Something else''. Hodja answered.

OUTWARD APPEARANCE.

Once Hodja was invited to a very important formal banquet, but he didn't dress up for the occasion but rather went in everyday clothing. Once there he was treated with disrespect and was looked upon with contempt. No one paid him any attention and the servants egnored him and didn't serve him dinner. After a short while he slipped out of the banquet unnoticed and went home. There he changed into his finest clothes, putting on his magnificent turban, a fine silk robe, very valuable jewelery, and a large expensie fur coat over all. Then he returned to the banquet.

This time he was received with open arms. The host himself bode hem to sit beside him at the highest seat and offered him a plate filled with the choicest delicacies. Much to their bewildered amazement, Hodja took off his coat, held it to the plate and said:

—Eat, my master, eat!

—Hodja, what are you doing? exclaimed his astonished host.

It is the clothes that you are giving these delicacies to, not the man inside!

IF I HAD THAT MUCH MONEY

Hodja went to the tailor one day and asked:
—This coat I have is too large for me, how much will it costt to have it taken in?
—Two pieces of gold, he replied.
This was quite a high price and Hodja was amazed and said:
—Come on, if I had that much money I would eat a lot of food so that my stomach would get bigger and then my coat would fit me just right!

I AM A STRANGER

One day Hodja went to a city. One of the citizens greeted Hodja and asked him. "What day is it today?"
 I swear I don't know, for I'ye just come to this city, and I haven't had enough time to learn its days yet". Hodja answered.

BY SINGING A SONG

One day an influential rich and powerful man from Akşehir lost his donkey. Town-criers immediately ran to the market and streets and began to look for that important man's donkey. They also asked Hodja to look for the donkey. But you know Hodja. He's always against receiving orders but he must manage somehow. He went to the vegetable gardens amongst the trees. He sang, built high hopes and wandered around.

The men who saw Hodja singing weer surprised and asked,

"How strange you are Hodja. What are you doing here alone?"

"I am looking for the donkey" Hodja said.

"Have you ever seen a man looking for a donkey by singing in vegetable gardens and under the trees just like you?" they asked.

Hodja was in trouble but found a way;

"Others look for other's donkeys by singing"

73

HE NEVER GOES BACK ON HIS WORD

One of his friends asked Hodja:
—How old are you?
—Forty, he replied.
—But you said the same thing when I asked you that three years ago!
—Yes, replied Hodja, I never go back on my word!

HE WILL LEAVE ME ALONE

Hodja Nasreddin had to stay in bed because of a serious illness. His health was quite bad, but he still made jokes.

His wife, realizing that he would not be cured, could not stop weeping. Hodja noticing his wife's position told her:

— Why are you weeping? Go and wash your face, then put on your best dress. Do not forget to put on your make up, too.

— But Hodja, said his wife, how can I do so when you are so ill? It is impossible.

— It is possible. I told you this because I know something. Ezrail, the angle of death, will come soon, so if the sees you beautiful I know he will like you and perhaps he will take you instead and will leave me alone.

OWING TO YOUR PRAYERS

Hodja was working as an apprentice in a tailor shop. One or two years after he began to work there, his mother asked him.

"What did you learn about your job, my dear? Tell me".

"Alright Mother, owing to your prayers I've learned half of the job.

I can now rip open sewn things easily."

He continued to speak to his mother's surprise;

"The other half of the job remains. If I live long enough, I will also learn how to sew them together."

YOU ARE RIGHT TOO

When Hodja Nasreddin was a judge in Akşehir, one day two men came in looking for help.

Hodja listened to one of the men. The man blamed the other and Hodja accepte his ideas:

— You are right, he said.

Hodja listened to the second man. This man blamed the other. Hodja realizing that he also put forward logi cal reasons said:

— You are right.

Hodja's wife used to listen at the trials. But she could not stand it any more and moved forward, saying:

— Hodja what kind of a judgement have you made? you say that both of the me are right. Would not it be real justice to decide which is quilty?

Hodja in a state of desperation looked towards her and said:

—Yes dear, you are right too!..

SOMETHING WORTH STEALING

One night a thief entered Hodja's house. Hodja hid in a cupboard, perhaps because he was frightened. The thief hadn't found anything worth stealing although he looked in every room. At the end he saw the cupboard and he wondered if there was something in it. He opened the door and saw that Hodja was in it.

"Oh, you're here?" he asked.

"Yes, I'm in the cupboard. I felt ashamed because I knew you wouldn't be able to find something worth stealing."

THE SOUND OF MONEY

There was a cook is Akşehir famous for his stinginess. One day he came to Hodja Nasreddin with a poor man and said:

— I was cooking my food in my shop and this man came in with a loaf of bread in his hand. He began to hold the bread in the steam of the cooking food and then to eat the loaf. When he finished I asked for the price of the food's vapour but he didn't accept this. Now I want to have my right.

Hodja turned towards the poor man and asked.

—Is he telling the truth?

The poor man answered:

— Yes Hodja, he tells the truth.

— Now give me your purse, said Hodja to the poor man.

The poor man gave it sadly, but there was nothing else to do, since Hodja was the judge. Hodja took the purse and shook it near the cook's ear.

— Now what did you hear? he said.

— The sound of money, said the cook.

Hodja then continued with a wise smile:

— Allright, now you have had your right. Take it and disappear quickly.

— But Hodja, said the cook. You did not give me any money.

Hodja looked at him with an angry face :

— What else do you expect? One who sells the vapour of food takes only the sound of money. Now take it and go.

COULD NOT LEARN TO ALIGHT

One day Hodja went to the forest to fetch some wood. When he was coming back with his donkey behind him, the donkey's leg slipped and it fell down a precipice.

Hodja looked down to see the donkey and sighed; My poor donkey finally learned how to fly but not to alight."

TO THINK OF SOUP!

One day Hodja was very hungry.

—If I just had a nice hot bowl of soup, he thought, I would be so content!

Just then someone knocked at the door. He opened it and there stood a young boy with an empty bowl in his hands. The boy said:

—My mother is not feeling well. Can you please give her a little hot soup?

—Oh, no! exclaimed Hodja. Not even my thoughts are my own. I anly have tc think of soup and my neighbours can smell it !

LIKE GOD OR A MAN

The children of the street had a lot of walnuts but nobody knew where they got them from. The children could not agree on the division of the walnuts they possessed. They began to fight and cry. At that time, Hodja was passing by when the quarrel was at its height. The children saw Hodja and ran to him and asked him to make a fair division.

They said,

"Hodja, make a fair division among us, please". Hodja called the children around him and held the walnuts.

"Do you want God's division or Man's division?"

The children said all together;

"God's division". Thereupon Hodja took a handful of walnuts and gave it to one of them. Then he gave two walnuts to another one and five or six to another, three handfuls to another and he gave nothing to some of them.

Thereupon the children began to object:

"What kind of a division is this? A lot to one of us, a few to some of us, and nothing to some of us, it is unjust, Hodja."

"Didn't you ask me to make God's division?. This is God's apportionment. He gives as he wishes. He gives less to one and much to the other, and he gives none to some, and men have to submit to their luck" he said.

I WAS INSIDE THE CLOAK

Like in every other house there were several âuarrels between Hodja Nasreddin and his wife. Sometimes there occured very fierce âuarrels between them.

One day, after such a fierce quarrel, Hodja went out with great anger, and a friend of his who was passing nearby saw him and asked what had happened the night before.

— You know, this happens in every house. We had a little fight at home last night.

— Yes, we heard it. But I coult not understand the great noise after the quarrel.

— Oh, you ask about that, said Hodja. While were fighting my wife got very angry and she hit my cloak and it rolled down the stairs.

Maybe that was the noise you have heard.

— But Hodja, said the man how can a cloak make such a noise when it rolls down the stairs? It is impossible.

Hodja answered back:

— Sure it did my friend, because "I" was it.

LET ME DIE

On another day of his illness Hodja was in quite bad shape. The only possible help might be from a doctor. But the matter was bothering the Hodja since he needed quite a big sum of money for the doctor and for the medicine that he would suggest.

Realiginz that there was no other possibility, Hodja accepted the idea of fetching a doctor. After the doctor's arrival he asked how much it would cost him for the visit and for medicine. The reply was 200 akces for being cured and becoming healthy as before.

Hodja then sent for the "Imam" of the village, and asked him the cost of burial. The man said :

— Oh Hodja, you are my friend, it can be donefor 10 akçes.

Then Hodja turned towards his wife and said :

— There is much difference as you see. It is better to settle the matter for 10 akçes instead of spending 200 for curing. Come on, my dear, pull the blanket over my head and let me die.

HOW TO SOOTHE A HEADACHE

·Someone asked Hodja "I have a headache, what should I do?"

Since Hodja felt suspicious about the man's character, he answered his question in this way.

"I have also had a toothache recently. They told me to have the tooth pulled out and this I did."

A LEARNED MAN

A farmer once brought Hodja a letter and asked him to read it to him.

— The handwriting is so bad that I can't read it, he said.

The man became angry and said:

— You wear the turban of a learned man and you can't even read a letter!

Hodja took off his turban and placed it before him and said:

— If you think that everyone who wears a turban is a learned man, then you put it on and see if you can read it:

THE SEA

One hot day Hodja was very thirsty. He went to the sea side, dipped his hands in and drank some water. Of course the salty water didn't quench his thrist at all, but rather made him more thristy. So he walked away from the sea until he found a freshwater spring. Then he drank and drank until his thrist was quenched. Then he filled his water-bag with water, returned to the sea, poured it in and said:

—You froth and foam and make so much noise for nothing. Now taste and see what real water is like!

DUCK SOUP.

Hodja was passing by a lake one day when he saw **a large number** of ducks swimming there. He was very hungry so he decided **to catch one and** have it for lunch. So Hodja quietly tiptoed towards them and **then dived to catch** one. But to his disapointment they all flew away and he was left **there went and hungry**. Then he sat down by the side of the lake, dipped a **piece of bread into the** lake and began eating it.

A friend passed by:

—Good afternoon, Hodja, what are you eating?

Duck soup, he replied.

LADDER FOR SALE

One day Hodja scaled a wall and pulled his ladder over into the garden on the other side. The owner caught him in his garden and shouted at him, saying:

Hey! What are you doing here?

—Well. I...am selling this ladder, improvised Hodja.

Fool, replied the landlord, you can't sell a ledder in a garden!

—Ah, it is you who are a fool! he wisely replied. For you don't know that a ladder can be sold absolutely anywhere!

IN HIS YOUTH

One day Hodja wanted to ride a horse. The horse was **too big** for him to ride so hi couldn't. "Oh youth, youth has passed away" he sighed loudly. Afterwards, looking around and seeing that there was no one around, he **murmured** to himself:
"I also know your youth."

ALL THINKS ARE POSSIBLE

One day Hodja's neighbour came to his house to have a chat with him. Hodja didn't want to talk to him so he told his wife to say that he wasn't home. The neihbour said:

—But I saw Hodja entering the house just a little while ago!

Hodja was sitting by the window listening to him. When he understood that the man didn'nt believe his wife he got every angry and opened the window and shouted:

—You foolish man! Doesnt't this house have both a front door and a back door? Isn't it possible that I could have gone out the back door?

One day, while Hodja was passing by a new barber's shop said to himself:

"My hair is getting very long. I haven't any business now, I'd better get my hair cut."

He went into the shop and he said to the barber. "Cut my hair so well that I'll always be your customer". Unfortunately the barber was both inexperienced and talkative, and also he thouhgt hide his mistakes he would by talking. I wish I hadn't came to this shop" thought Hodja.

Don't worry Hodja, it will be a good haircut the barber said and began to use a razor. At the beginning he cut somewhere on Hodja's head and he put some cotton wool on the place he cut.

"I am the most successful barber here abouts" said the barber and went on cutting hair and putting cotton wool on as if nothing had happened.

"Why are you afraid of getting your hair cut Hodja?. You know, it isn't an easy job. This is my father's occupation. Who will cut hair if we don't cut it?" the barber said to Hodja.

"How marvel ous. Look at the beauty of this head" the barber said.

"What is it to your if my head is beautiful? Hey you, my head looks like a cotton field, as if that isn't enough, you are talking about beauty. " Hodja shouted at him.

Later, Hodja understood that this man will bring trouble upon his head. He took his robe and his turban, and he let himself out. When the barber shouted at him, running behind, he said:

"Where are you going, Hodja? your haircut hasn't been finished yet.

Hodja turned to the barber and said,

"Barber Effendi, you sowed cotton on one half of my head, I'll sow flax seed on the other half of my head and he walked away.

II

One day Hodja had some business in the court. When he learned that the judge didn't to anything unless he was given a present, he paused and pondered.

When he decided that there was no other way than giving a present, he took a large pot and went to the river side. He filled the pot with earth and put some honey on the earth.

In the evening when it became dark he went to the judge's house taking the pot with him. He thought the judge would be very glad when he saw so much honey and do his business.

Hodja knocked at the door and when he heard the judge say: "Who is it? I'm coming" Hodja said "It is me, Nasreddin Hodja. I came to take decree in Writing."

When the judge opened the door, he saw Hodja with a pot of honey in his hands. His mouth began to water when he saw the pot of honey. The judge took it without saying anything and then he put the paper in Hodja's hand.

Hodja went far away as soon as the judge gave the paper, because Hodja thought that if the judge learned that there was earth under the honey, he would give Hodja a lesson, but Hodja could not give a lesson to the judge.

A few days later, one of the court ushers came to Hodja and said. "The judge sent you his greetings and said that there was a mistake in the decree that must be corrected.

Hodja laughed and said to the usher. "Effendi, you must have heard it wrong there wasn't a mistake the decree, perhaps there might have been a mistake in the pot of honey.

III

One day while Hodja was on the way home he saw that a lot of people were going into and coming out of a mansion.

As it is well-known that Hodja was a curious man. He couldn't stand that witho-ut learning what was happenning.

He saw a man standing by the door, and asked him what was happening inside.
''There is a wedding celebration'' he said.

As soon as Hodja heard the world "wedding", fried chickens, turkeys and trays of rice came into his mind. Hodja.

"Thanks, friend" he said and immediately he planned a trick.

After he found a piece of paper and put it into an envelope, he took the envelope to the wedding house. To the servant at the door.

He said. "I must see your master at once, I brought a letter for him."

The man servant at once guided Hodja and took him to the master.
"Good luck with your wedding and excuse me because I came in," he said and gave the letter to the master.

Hodja sat down and started eating as soon as possible. After the master looked over the envelope he said.

"Isn't there a mistake Hodja? There isn't anything written on the envelope.

Without raising his head, Hodja answered
"Excuse me, I did it in a hurry and therefore carelessly, as you will see, there isn't anything written on the paper in the envelope either."

IV

On a hot summer day, a beggar was begging in the deserted streets of Akşehir, saying "Alms for the poor for God's Sake".

Meanwhile Hodja was replacing the broken tiles on his roof in preparation for the next winter.

While Hodja was working someone knocked at the door. The man who knocked was a stranger. Before Hodja had asked the man what he wanted, the man asked Hodja to come down.

"I'll tell you something very important" he said.

For that reason Hodja stopped working to go down, anxious to learn what the man would tell him that was so important.

When Hodja descended, grumbling from the heat and tiredness, the stranger extended his hand to Hodja and begged,

"An alms please, Hodja, for God's sake."

Hodja got very angry with the man but he tried to keep calm. He walked towards the ladder and said to the man.

"Let's get to the top first."

Before they climbed the roof the beggar began to say "The Lord save you, Hodja" "Long live Hodja" expecting to get better alms.

When they climbed up the ladder and reached the roof dead tired, at last Hodja turned to face the beggar and said.

"Now we are quits, God help you. You can go away now.

ONE DAY HODJA WENT TO THE FOREST TO CUT PINE TREES

WELL, THAT IS ENOUGH FOR TODAY

IT IS SAID THAT PINE CATCHES FIRE EASILY. I WONDER IF THAT IS TRUE

IT WOULD BE EASY TO LEARN IF I IT ONCE TRIED

AAii Aii Aii Aii

WHAT A PITY THE DONKEY WILL CATCH FIRE. OH ! STOP

I TOLD YOU STOP FOOLISH DONKEY, I CAN'T RUN BEHIND YOU ANY MORE

SINCE YOU WILL NOT WAIT FOR ME, IF YOU ARE CLEVER RUN TOWARDS THE LAKE

ONE DAY HODJA WAS WALKING ON THE STREET QUIETEY.

EXCUSE ME, YOU LOOK LIKE ONE OF MY FRIENDS.

OH, STOP WHAT ARE YOU DOING HODJA.

WE ARE GOING TO THE COURT. THERE WE'LL SETTLE UP WITH YOU.

WHILE I WAS WALKING QUIETLY ON THE STREET THIS MAN SLAPPED MY NECK I AM BRINGING A LAWSUIT AGAINST HIM KADI EFENDI.

OH HODJA IT ISN'T SO IMPORTANT AS TO BRING A LAWSUIT. BRING TWO COINS AND MAKE PEACE.

AT ONCE I WILL FETCH THEM.

THREE HOURS PASSED, BUT THE MAN DIDN'T RETURN. HE FOOLED YOU NASREDDIN.

FIRST TAKE THIS SLAP KADI EFFENDI

NOW, THE MAN CAN PAY YOU TWO COINS GOODBYE.

125

ONA DAY HODJA WANTED TO EAT WATERMELON AND HE WENT IN HIS NEIGHBOUR'S VEGETABLE GARDEN.

NICE, I HAVE A STRONG DESIRE TO EAT THEM.

IF I PUT THEM IN THIS SACK I CAN EAT THEM WITH MORE OF AN APPETITE AT HOME.

IT'S NOT THAT EASY. WHAT ARE YOU DOING HERE?

HOW DID YOU GO INTO MY VEGETABLE GARDEN?

OH MY NEIGHBOUR QUIET PLEASE. I DIDN'T COME HERE BY MY SELF THE WIND BLEW ME INTO THE GARDEN.

OH THE WIND BLEW YOU? WHO PICKED THE MELONS THEN?

THE WIND BLEW SO STRONG THAT WHATEVER I HOLD I PICKED?

I ACCEPT THAT TOO, BUT WHO PUT THEM IN THE SACK?

GOD BLESS YOU MY FRIEND, THAT'S WHAT I WAS PONDERING SITTING HERE.

TAKE IT MY DEAR, THE THREE KILOS OF MEAT AND COOK A DELICIOUS STEW FOR DINNER.

ALRIGHT HODJA

HODJA'S WIFE COOKED ALL THE MEAT AND SHE ATE ITT WITH HER FRIENDS

I HOPE MY WIFE HAS ALREADY COOKED THE STEW.

WHAT IS THAT SOUP HATUN? WHERE IS THE STEW?

I COULDN'T COOK STEW BECAUSE THE CAT ATE ALL THE MEAT.

OH, IS THAT SO? THE CAT ATE THE MEAT? WELL, BRING ME THE WEIGHING SCALE.

THIS CAT IS THREE KILOS IN WEIGHT. IF THIS IS THE CAT WHERE IS THE MEAT? IF THIS IS MEAT, WHERE IS THE CAT?

ONE DAY HODJA KILLS A GOOSE TO TAKE TO TAMERLANE AND FRIES IT, PUTS IT ON A TRAY AND SETS OUT TO THE PALACE

IT SMELLS DELICIOUS NOBODY CAN SMELL IT WITHOUT EATING IT

HE'LL NEVER SEE THE ABSENT LEG.

IN THE PRESENCE OF TAMERLANE

WHAT A STRANGE GOOSE IS THIS HODJA? WHERE IS ITS OTHER LEG?

ALL THE GEESE HAVE ONLY ONE LEG IN AKŞEHİR. IF YOU DON'T BELIEVE ME, LOOK AT THE GEESE IN THE GARDEN PLEASE.

YOU, GUARD, FRIGHTEN THOSE GEESE.

DID YOU SEE, THEY HAVE TWO LEGS LIKE YOU AND THEY RUN VERY WELL.

IF YOU SAW A SPEAR LIKE THAT YOU ALSO WOULD RUN LIKE A MAN WITH FOUR LEGS, MY SULTAN

129

ONE DAY WHILE HODJA WAS WANDERING IN THE BAZAAR TO DO SOME SHOPPING.

WHERE HAVE YOU BEEN HODJA? I'M VERY GLAD TO SEE YOU AGAIN.

EXCUSE ME BUT WHAT DAY IS IT TODAY?

HOW DID I COME ACROSS THIS STICKY MAN?

HOW COULD I KNOW WHAT DAY IT IS TODAY. I AM A STRANGER.

BUT, HODJA WHAT NONSENSE YOU SAY. TO BE A STRANGER IN THIS CITY DOESN'T MEAN THAT YOU'LL NOT KNOW DAY IT IS TODAY.

PERHAPS YOU WOULDN'T KNOW EITHER, IF I ASKED YOU IN WHICH MONTH WE ARE NOW.

OF COURSE, I WOULDN'T. DO YOU THINK I'M BUYING AND SELLING "DATES" IN THE BAZAAR?

ONE DAY HODJA'S FRIENDS GATHERED AND WANTED TO PLAY A TRICK ON HODJA

ALRIGHT, HE'S COMING NOW. LET'S DO EVERYTHING AS WE PLANNED BEFORE.

WELL, HODJA, YOU KNOW THAT CLEANLINESS COMES FROM BELIEF. WE THOUGHT THAT WE HAD BETTER GO TO BATH AND WASH

OF COURSE, LET'S GO.

HERE IS THE BEST BATH IN THE CITY HODJA, WHAT DO YOU SAY?

VERY GOOD. LET'S ENTER AT ONCE.

HAMAM

COME CLOSER EFFENDI, I HAVE A SUGGESTION. ALL OF US WILL LAY AN EGG AND THE ONE THAT CANNOT LAY AN EGG, WILL PAY THE BATH FEES OF ALL OF US.

CACKLE, CACKLE, MY EGG IS HOT.

CACKLE, CACKLE, THIS ONE IS MINE

THEY PLANNED A TRICK BEFORE, BUT THEY WILL SEE WHAT I WILL DO TO THEM

ÜRRRRÜRÜÜÜÖÖöööoo

HODJA HAVE YOU GONE CRAZY? WHY DO YOU CROW LIKE A COCK?

YOU CACKLED AND LAID EGGS. ISN'T A COCK NECESSARY FOR THREE HENS?

ONE DAY HODJA WENT TO HUNT TAKING A FRIEND WITH HIM.

PSSST! ONLY THE CUBS ARE IN THE CAVE. THE MOTHER ISN'T IN THE CAVE.

GIROOORRR

A SMELL OF FLESH IS COMING TO MY NOSE PROBABLY A HUMAN WENT INTO MY CAVE.

OH MY GOD. IT IS GOING INTO THE CAVE IT WILL KILL FRIEND.

STOP, DON'T GO THERE.

HODJA, WHAT ARE YOU DOING THERE. IS THAT YOU MAKING THAT FUSS OUT SIDE.

SHUT UP AND START PRAYING IF HIS TAIL ISN'T STRONG ENOUGH THEN YOU WILL SEE THE REAL FUSS!

ON A HOT SUMMER DAY, HODJA HAD SET OUT ON HIS WAY. HE WAS TERRIBLY THIRSTY. AT THAT MOMENT, HE CAME BEFORE A FOUNTAIN.

OH A FOUNTAIN AT LAST I CAN STOP MY THIRST

OH GOD! WHY DID THEY THRUST THIS PIECE OF WOOD INTO THIS TAB?

I AM PULLING IT WITH ALL MY MIGHT BUT I CAN'T TAKE IT OUT.

HOHOHOOP!

I TOOK OUT THE STAKE BUT I GOT WET.

I'VE JUST UNDERSTOOD WHY THEY THRUST THIS PIECE OF WOOD INTO YOU IN MY OPINION IT IS TOO SMALL FOR A CRAZY MAN LIKE YOU

THROUGH GIVING FOOD TO THE DONKEY, HODJA AND HIS WIFE START QUARRELLING.

OF COURSE YOU'LL GIVE FOOD TO THE DONKEY TODAY

WHY DON'T YOU GIVE THE FOOD?

ALRIGHT, I HAVE A SUGGESTION THEN. THE ONE WHO SPEAKS FIRST, WILL GIVE THE FOOD

ALRIGHT.

PERHAPS I DON'T KEEP CALM THE BEST THING TO DO IS TO GO TO MY NEIGHBER.

SHE CAN'T STAND NOT SPE AKING TILL THE EVENING. I'M SURE SHE'LL SPEAK

OH, THERE ARE VALU ABLE THINGS I AM VERY LUCKY

HE SAW ME WHEN I WAS STEALING THE THINGS BUT HE DIDN'T EVEN LOOK AT ME. HE MUST BE MAD.

GOODBYE. YOU DIDN'T SAY ANYTHING WHILE I WAS STEALING, THANK YOU.

WHEN HODJA'S WIFE CAME HOME.

WHAT IS GOING ON HERE HODJA? THEY ROBBED THE HOUSE.

WHY ARE YOU CRYING MY WIFE? YOU LOST THE BET. GO AND GIVE FOOD TO THE DONKEY.

HODJA SETS OUT ON THE WAY TO VISIT HIS FRIEND IN THE NEARBY VILLAGE ON A HOT SUMMER DAY.

OH HODJA. WHAT A TERRIBLE STATE YOU ARE IN YOU GOT SUNSTROKE. LET'S GO TO MY HOUSE AND DRINK COLD FRUIT JUICE.

TAKE THIS SPOON TO DRINK THE FRUIT JUICE.

OH, REALLY IT'S GOOD FRUIT JUICE, BUT I CAN'T TASTE ENOUGH BECAUSE THIS SPOON IS TOO SMALL.

OH. I AM FULL. HOW WONDERFUL!

HE TOOK A BIG SPOON, AND HE WAS FULL QUICKLY, NOT TO FEEL ASHAMED HE SAYS HE IS FULL.

OH MY GOD, WHAT DELICIOUS FRUIT JUICE AND IT IS VERY COLD. OH, I CAN DIE

ENOUGH FRIEND. GIVE ME THAT BIG SPOON SO THAT I TOO CAN DIE OF FRUIT JUICE WITH FULL ENJOYMENT.

HODJA WAS PUTTING A STONE INTO A POT TO COUNT THE DAYS IN RAMAZAN

IF I PUT THIS STONE IN THE POT, IT IS GOING TO BE THE THIRD DAY OF RAMAZAN

HODJA WENT AWAY. BRING THE STONES

HODJA WILL BE VERY SURPRISED

WHICH DAY OF RAMAZAN IS IT TODAY?

JUST A MINUTE, I CAN GO AND LEARN NOW.

ALAS, ONE HUNDRED AND FORTY TWO STONES I COUNTED. THIS YEAR RAMAZAN TOOK MANY DAYS.

I WENT HOME AND LEARNED. TODAY IS THE FIFTIETH DAY OF RAMAZAN

BUT HODJA, YOU KNOW THAT RAMAZAN CAN NEVER BE MORE THAN THIRTY DAYS.

YOU MUST THANK ME, ACCORDING TO MY POT IT IS THE ONE HUNDRED AND FORTY SECOND DAY OF RAMAZAN NOT THE FIFTIETH DAY OF IT.

138

A MISER FRIEND OF HODJA INVITED HIM TO EAT.

"I WISH I HADN'T INVITED HIM"

"OH, THE FOOD WAS SO DELICIOUS THAT I CANNOT HAVE ENOUFH OF ITS TASTE"

OH, HONEY IS COMING TOO. I LIKE IT VERY MUCH"

EVERYBODY LIKES IT IF IT IS FREE.

OH VERY NICE. VERY NICE. IF I PUT HONEY ON THESE PIECES OF BREAD, THEY ARE MORE DELICIOUS LIKE THAT.

OH MY GOD, HE HASN'T BECOME SATIATED YET. HE FINISHED ALL THE HONEY.

I THINK I PUT ENOUGH HONEY ON THEM. NOW I CAN EAT THEM TOO.

DON'T EAT THEM EITHER HODJA, GOOD KNOWS, YOUR STOMACH WILL BURN!

GET LOST. AFTER I FINISH THESE THEN WE'LL SEE WHO WILL BURN

139

ALI AGHA WAS KNOW AS A MISER AND HODJA NEVER LIKED HIM. ONE DAY.

HODJA WOULD YOU LIKE LEND ME YOUR CLOTHESLINE PLEASE? MY WIFE NEEDS IT TO HANG THE CLOTHES.

I CAN GIVE IT BUT I MUST ASK MY WIFE FIRST.

WAIT A MINUTE HERE I'LL COME BACK AFTER I'VE ASKED HER.

SNICKER SNICKER

I'LL ALSO BE ABLE TO USE THE CLOTHESLINE WITHOUT PAYING.

I'M SORRY YOU HAD TO FOR ME BUT I WON'T BE ABLE TO LEND THE CLOTHESLINE BECAUSE MY WIFE HAS SPERAD FLOUR OUT ON IT

IF YOU DON'T WANT TO LEND IT THAT'S ALRIGHT, BUT WHY DO YOU WANT TO MAKE FUN OF ME? HOW CAN SHE SPREAD OUT FLOUR ON A CLOTHESLINE?

WHY ARE YOU SHOUTING AT ME? IF I DON'T WANT TO LEND IT I CAN SPREAD EITHER FLOUR OR WATER ON IT, IT'S NO CONCERN OF YOURS.

WHEN HODJA SAW HUMAN BEINGS BAD HABITS HE USED TO GO TO A CEMETERY.

HOW WONDERFUL, THE SILENCE OF THIS CEMETERY GIVES ME INCREDIBLE PEACE.

ALAS! THE FORTY ROBBERS THE ARE COMING, I MUST HIDE.

STOP! WE'LL HAVE A REST IN THIS CEMETERY.

I'M TO LATE TO ESCAPE. THE BEST THING TO DO IS TO GET DOWN INTO THIS GRAVE.

I SHOULD TAKE OFF MY CLOTHES, THEN THEY CANNOT STEAL THEM IF THEY CATCH ME.

ALAS! THEY ARE COMING HERE.

CHIEF! CHIEF! LOOK THERE'S SOMEONE IN THAT GRAVE.

HEY YOU! ARE YOU A HUMAN BEING OR A SPIRIT?

I DIED FIVE YEARS AGO. I'VE JUST RETURNED TO SEE WHAT IS GOING ON HERE.

HELP, RUN FOR YOUR LIFE A DEAD MAN RETURNED TO LIFE.